THE GREAT BIBLE DISCOVERY

INTO THE PROMISED LAND

THE BIBLE IS A BEST-SELLER. IT IS ALSO ONE OF THE MASTER-WORKS OF WORLD LITERATURE - SO IMPORTANT THAT UNIVERSITIES TODAY TEACH 'NON-RELIGIOUS' BIBLE COURSES TO HELP STUDENTS WHO CHOOSE TO STUDY WESTERN LITERATURE.

THE BIBLE POSSESSES AN AMAZING POWER TO FASCINATE YOUNG AND OLD ALIKE.

ONE REASON FOR THIS UNIVERSAL APPEAL IS THAT IT DEALS WITH BASIC HUMAN LONGINGS, EMOTIONS, RELATIONSHIPS. 'ALL THE WORLD IS HERE.' ANOTHER REASON IS THAT SO MUCH OF THE BIBLE CONSISTS OF STORIES. THEY ARE FULL OF MEANING BUT EASY TO REMEMBER.

HERE ARE THOSE STORIES, PRESENTED SIMPLY AND WITH A MINIMUM OF EXPLANATION. WE HAVE LEFT THE TEXT TO SPEAK FOR ITSELF. GIFTED ARTISTS USE THE ACTION-STRIP TECHNIQUE TO BRING THE BIBLE'S DEEP MESSAGE TO READERS OF ALL AGES. THEIR DRAWINGS ARE BASED ON INFORMATION FROM ARCHAEOLOGICAL DISCOVERIES COVERING FIFTEEN CENTURIES.

AN ANCIENT BOOK - PRESENTED FOR THE PEOPLE OF THE SECOND MILLENNIUM. A RELIGIOUS BOOK - PRESENTED FREE FROM THE INTERPRETATION OF ANY PARTICULAR CHURCH. A UNIVERSAL BOOK - PRESENTED IN A FORM THAT ALL MAY ENJOY.

M publishing
CARLISLE, UK

5

As they made their way towards Canaan the Hebrews faced problems. Perhaps the most obvious was the need for food and water. But there were also human obstacles. People lived wherever the land was fertile and local leaders were not at all happy at the arrival of a large body of foreigners, even if they said they were only passing by. The story shows that they used all sorts of methods to oppose these new arrivals.

As for Canaan itself - it seemed amazingly fertile and prosperous to the Hebrews, who were accustomed to living a hard life in the desert. What a wonderful future lay before them! But the land was already occupied. There was fighting to be done. And Moses had died.

His successor, Joshua, is not very well-known as a biblical character. (His name re-appears in the New Testament in its Greek form as 'Jesus'.) But he had a heavy responsibility. Moses had been a strong leader - could Joshua be as effective? The situation he faced was quite new - attacking the fortified towns (the Bible calls them cities if they had walls) of Canaan and then dividing the land among the twelve tribes. But he knew that the same God who had given wisdom and strength to Moses would be with him too.

Joshua also realised the importance to Israel of their relationship with God. Once the nation had occupied most of Canaan he sent for all the tribal leaders and reminded them of the choice they must make. They were in a country full of gods and goddesses, their ancestors had worshipped idols in Ur. Now they must choose. Would they promise to stay faithful to the God of Abraham, Isaac and Jacob, who had made a covenant with them at Sinai?

In this way, as they settled in the Promised Land, the twelve tribes renewed their covenant with God.

NUMBERS
DEUTERONOMY 6
JOSHUA

INTO THE PROMISED LAND

First published as *Découvrir la Bible* 1983

First edition © Librairie Larousse 1983
English translation © Daan Retief Publishers 1990
24-volume series adaptation by Mike Jacklin © Knowledge Unlimited 1994
This edition © OM Publishing 1995

01 00 99 98 97 96 95   7 6 5 4 3 2 1

OM Publishing is an imprint of Send the Light Ltd.,
P.O. Box 300, Carlisle, Cumbria CA3 0QS, U.K.

Series editor: D. Roy Briggs
English translation: Bethan Uden
Introductions: Peter Cousins

British Library Cataloguing in Publication Data
A catalogue record for this book is available from the British Library
ISBN 1-85078-209-1

Printed in Singapore by Tien Wah Press (Pte) Ltd.

THE AMALEKITES AND THE CANAANITES CAME DOWN FROM THE HILL-COUNTRY...

THEY DEFEATED THE ISRAELITES AND CHASED THEM AS FAR AS HORMAH.

A CURSE ON YOU WOMEN WHO GAVE BIRTH TO REBELLIOUS SONS! THEY'VE ONLY BROUGHT DEATH!

THE ISRAELITES TURNED BACK TO THE SOUTH, AS FAR AS KADESH.

SOON AFTERWARDS...

MOSES, THE PEOPLE ARE COMPLAINING ABOUT YOU AGAIN.

WHY DID YOU MAKE THE CHILDREN OF ISRAEL DIE?

TO REBEL IS TO CHOOSE DEATH!

THE ONLY ONE WHO CAN LEAD ISRAEL IS THE ONE THE LORD HAS APPOINTED.

THEN MOSES ASKED EACH TRIBE TO BRING TO THE TENT A STAFF BEARING ITS LEADER'S NAME. AARON'S NAME WOULD BE ON LEVI'S STAFF.

THE NEXT DAY MOSES TOOK THE TWELVE STAFFS OUT OF THE TENT, AND SHOWED THEM TO THE PEOPLE...

LORD, GIVE US A SIGN! SHOW US WHOM YOU'VE CHOSEN!

THE LORD HAS CHOSEN AARON'S STAFF.

TRUST THE LEVITES, THE BROTHERS OF AARON, WHO MAKE OFFERINGS FOR YOU.

THE PEOPLE STAYED IN THE OASIS OF KADESH FOR SEVERAL YEARS, MOVING AROUND, BUT COMING TOGETHER FOR THE GREAT FESTIVALS.

THERE MIRIAM SAID FAREWELL TO HER BELOVED BROTHER MOSES, AND DIED. SHE WAS BURIED THERE.

SOON THERE WAS NO WATER...

TAKE US OUT OF THIS DESERT!

WHY DID YOU MAKE US LEAVE EGYPT?

WHAT DO YOU EXPECT ME TO ASK THE LORD? MUST I MAKE WATER COME OUT OF THIS ROCK?

MOSES STRUCK THE ROCK TWICE.

COME! SING FOR JOY TO THE LORD!

HE'S THE ROCK WHO SAVES US!

AT KADESH MOSES CALLED THE LEADERS OF THE TRIBES TOGETHER AND PERSUADED THEM TO CONTINUE THE JOURNEY TO THE PROMISED LAND.

WE'LL GO NORTH-EAST AND ROUND THE DEAD SEA.

BUT THEN WE'LL HAVE TO GO THROUGH THE LAND OF EDOM*.

EDOM'S OUR BROTHER... PERHAPS HE'LL LET US PASS THROUGH...

LET'S SEND A MESSENGER TO HIM!

BUT WE'LL PASS THROUGH QUICKLY, WITHOUT STOPPING...

AND I SAY, NO! AT LAST ESAU HAS HIS REVENGE ON JACOB!

IT'S USELESS TO INSIST! THEY'LL BAR OUR WAY...

THEN WE'LL GO ROUND EDOM! WE'LL GO EAST, THROUGH THE DESERT!

* Edom was descended from Esau, the brother Jacob had wronged.

BUT AARON COULDN'T GO ANY FURTHER...

MOSES, MY TIME HAS COME, I CAN'T GO ON!

11

THE ISRAELITES SETTLED IN THE PLAINS OF MOAB, ACROSS THE RIVER FROM JERICHO.

AT THE PALACE OF BALAK, KING OF MOAB...

THEY WIPED OUT THE AMORITES... AND IF THEY DECIDE TO ATTACK US, WE'LL ALSO BE DESTROYED...

ISRAEL'S STRENGTH IS THEIR GOD... A BIGGER ARMY WON'T HELP AGAINST HIM.

SO, WHAT DO YOU SUGGEST?

BALAAM'S THE GREATEST OF ALL THE SEERS. HE KNOWS THE GOD OF THE HEBREWS. HIS CURSE WILL DEFEAT ISRAEL.

THE LEADING MOABITES TRAVELLED TOWARDS THE EUPHRATES TO GET BALAAM TO HELP...

16

MEANWHILE, IN THE CAMP OF ISRAEL...

WHEN WE'VE CROSSED THE JORDAN, THE LAND WILL BE SHARED OUT AMONG YOU.

WE WANT TO STAY HERE.

THIS COUNTRY IS GOOD FOR STOCK-FARMING. WE'LL LIVE WELL.

REUBEN! GAD! AFTER SUCH A JOURNEY ARE YOU GIVING UP SO CLOSE TO THE END?

LOT ALSO THOUGHT HE'D MADE A GOOD CHOICE!

MY GOD! DON'T REJECT THESE CHILDREN...

SO BE IT! YOUR FAMILIES AND YOUR FLOCKS CAN STAY HERE, BUT YOUR FIGHTING MEN MUST COME WITH US!

17

MEANWHILE BALAAM WAS ON HIS WAY FROM THE EUPHRATES TO MOAB AND KING BALAK. THE STORY OF THE TROUBLE HE HAD WITH HIS DONKEY IS MOST AMUSING...

WHY DON'T YOU OBEY ME?

WHAT HAVE I DONE TO MAKE YOU BEAT ME?

A BIT FURTHER ON...

OW!

I'D KILL YOU IF I COULD!

AREN'T I YOUR DONKEY? YOU KNOW ME WELL!

WHY DID YOU HIT YOUR DONKEY? I CAME TO BAR YOUR PATH, THE DONKEY SAW ME, AND IT TURNED ASIDE FROM ME THREE TIMES.

I DIDN'T SEE YOU. IF YOU THINK MY JOURNEY IS WRONG, I'LL TURN BACK.

GO ON, BUT SAY ONLY WHAT I TELL YOU.

19

BUT KING BALAK DIDN'T GIVE UP...

NOT PHYSICAL FORCE, NOT WORDS FROM SEERS... WHAT THEN?

SEDUCE THEM!

THEY'RE MEN LIKE ALL THE REST... OUR GIRLS KNOW HOW TO PLEASE THEM AND MAKE THEM 'FORGET THEIR GOD.

... STRANGE HUTS APPEARED NEAR TO THE ISRAELITE CAMPS...

IT'S LINEN! THE BEST... BUT I'VE EVEN BETTER MATERIAL INSIDE...

YOU'RE MORE HANDSOME LIKE THAT!

AND YOU, YOU'RE BEAUTIFUL!

GRADUALLY THE MOABITE WOMEN TURNED THE ISRAELITE MEN AWAY FROM THEIR GOD.

LORD! MUST I PLEAD FOR YOUR PARDON OR YOUR ANGER?

* Hebrew word meaning 'That's right', 'Agreed!'

MOSES CLIMBED MOUNT NEBO,
WHICH LOOKS OVER THE PROMISED LAND...

THERE, IN THE LAND OF MOAB,
MOSES DIED.
GOD TOOK THE BREATH FROM
THE MOUTH OF HIS PROPHET.

'THERE HAS NEVER
BEEN A PROPHET IN ISRAEL
LIKE MOSES:
THE LORD SPOKE WITH
HIM FACE TO FACE!'

Deuteronomy 34:10

CARLO MARCELLO 82

AND STILL TO THIS DAY
NOBODY KNOWS WHERE HIS GRAVE IS...

JOSHUA

NO ONE WILL BE ABLE TO STAND AGAINST YOU AS LONG AS YOU LIVE; I WILL BE WITH YOU AS I WAS WITH MOSES; I WILL NOT LEAVE YOU ALONE. BE STRONG AND TAKE COURAGE!

SCENARIO: Etienne DAHLER • DRAWING: Pierre FRISANO

WHAT WILL HAPPEN TO US WITHOUT MOSES?

GOD WILL GO ON GUIDING US. WE'VE JOSHUA.

AND WE'VE THE TORAH.* WE MUST OBEY IT.

*The Law of Moses.

THEIR DONKEY? THAT'S IT THERE!

JUST STONES! THAT'S FUNNY!

THE NEWS QUICKLY REACHED THE KING.

HEBREWS! ARREST THEM!

MEANWHILE, AT RAHAB'S...

WHERE CAN WE SPEND THE NIGHT?

YOU MEAN: WHERE CAN YOU HIDE?

BUT...

UP TO THE ROOF! QUICKLY!

AND YOU, GET LOST!

NO SOONER WERE THEY HIDDEN...

YES, THEY ATE HERE, BUT THEY LEFT JUST BEFORE THE CITY GATES WERE CLOSED AT SUNSET.

WHY DID YOU SAVE OUR LIVES?

I SAW THAT YOU WERE HEBREWS. EVERYBODY HERE IS TERRIFIED THAT YOU'LL ATTACK US...

... YOUR GOD IS THE GREATEST OF ALL GODS. WHEN JERICHO FALLS INTO YOUR HANDS, REMEMBER TONIGHT AND SAVE MY FAMILY.

I SWEAR IT TO YOU. TIE A RED CORD TO YOUR WINDOW, AND NONE OF OUR PEOPLE WILL HARM YOU.

THEN THE TWO SPIES, SODI AND GADDIEL, RETURNED SAFELY TO THEIR CAMP.

FAR UP THE RIVER, THE CLIFFS AT THE VILLAGE OF ADAM COLLAPSED, AND THE WATER WAS DAMMED UP, LEAVING THE RIVER-BED DRY.

WHEN ALL THE PEOPLE HAD CROSSED, THE JORDAN STARTED TO FLOW AGAIN.

WHEN THEY REACHED GILGAL*, JOSHUA HAD THE STONES SET UP IN A CIRCLE...

... SO THAT ALL THE PEOPLES OF THE EARTH WILL REMEMBER GOD'S POWER.

THE PROMISE MADE TO ABRAHAM HAS COME TRUE.

AND TOMORROW JERICHO WILL BE OURS!

NO...

... IN THREE DAYS' TIME IT'S PASSOVER. WE'LL STRIKE AFTER THAT.

*In Hebrew: circle of stones.

BUT IN THAT TIME ALL THE KINGS OF THE COUNTRY WILL ATTACK US!

HAVE FAITH, URI!

JOSHUA WAS RIGHT. THE CANAANITE KINGS CONSULTED TOGETHER, BUT...

AS LONG AS THEIR GOD IS ON THEIR SIDE, IT'S HOPELESS TO TAKE ANY ACTION.

THE FIRST PASSOVER IN THE PROMISED LAND.

BE BLESSED, ETERNAL GOD, KING OF THE UNIVERSE, WHO GAVE US LIFE, AND HAS LET US SEE THIS DAY!

NOW THE LORD GIVES JERICHO TO US! DO AS HE'S TOLD US.

THERE THEY ARE! TAKE UP YOUR POSITIONS!

THEY CARRIED THE COVENANT BOX ROUND THE CITY ONCE, THEN THE ISRAELITES RETURNED TO THEIR CAMP...

THE DEFENDERS OF AI DROVE THE ISRAELITES BACK AND KILLED SOME OF THEM.

LORD! WHY DID YOU BRING US ALL THIS WAY, TO LET US DIE?

ISRAEL HAS SINNED...?

חָטָא יִשְׂרָאֵל*

AT JERICHO SOME PEOPLE KEPT SOME OF THE BOOTY FOR THEMSELVES. THAT'S WHY THE LORD DIDN'T SAVE US YESTERDAY.

FROM THE CROWD JOSHUA PICKED OUT THE GUILTY PERSON.

WE FOUND THAT IN HIS TENT!

ACHAN, MEN PAID FOR YOUR GREED WITH THEIR LIVES!

PUT HIM TO DEATH!

* Israel has sinned.

THE NEXT DAY JOSHUA PICKED OUT THE BEST OF HIS TROOPS AND TOLD THEM HIS PLAN OF ATTACK.

THIS TIME GOD WILL DELIVER AI TO US!

DON'T TRY TO FIGHT. WHEN THEY COME OUT, RUN AWAY FROM THEM.

THE PEOPLE OF AI DID JUST AS JOSHUA EXPECTED: THEY CHASED AFTER HIM...

THERE'S JOSHUA'S SIGN! LET'S GO! BRING THE TORCHES!

... LEAVING NO SOLDIERS TO DEFEND THE TOWN.

OUR TOWN IS ON FIRE!

CURSED BE ANYONE WHO MAKES OR WORSHIPS AN IDOL! CURSED BE ANYONE WHO DOES NOT KEEP THE COMMANDMENTS OF THE LORD!

AMEN! WE AGREE!

AMEN! WE AGREE!

YOU'VE CHOSEN TO SERVE THE LORD!

GET RID OF THE FOREIGN GODS!

THE CANAANITES WERE AFRAID WHEN THEY LEARNED THAT THE TRIBES OF ISRAEL HAD FORMED AN ALLIANCE.

OUR TOWN OF GIBEON IS IN GREAT DANGER...

...LET'S JOIN THOSE WHO ARE AGAINST ISRAEL!

THEY HAVEN'T A HOPE!

...AND IF WE TRY TO MAKE PEACE?

ISRAEL WOULD NEVER AGREE TO IT!

WELL, THEN, LET'S TRY A TRICK!

SOME TIME LATER TWO MEN FROM GIBEON CAME TO THE ISRAELITE CAMP AT GILGAL.

WE COME FROM A COUNTRY FAR AWAY. WE'VE HEARD OF YOUR GOD...

OUR PEOPLE WANT TO SERVE HIM AND YOU.

GOOD! IN RETURN WE'LL PROTECT YOU. GO IN PEACE.

THREE DAYS LATER...

JOSHUA, HERE ARE THE GREAT TRAVELLERS! THEY LIED TO US. THEY'RE FROM GIBEON.

HAVE PITY, JOSHUA! WE WERE SO AFRAID THAT YOU'D DESTROY OUR TOWN.

RIGHT! I'LL KEEP MY PROMIS BUT FROM NOW ON YOU'LL BE OUR SLAVES.

ONE BY ONE THE TOWNS OF GIBEON, CHEPHIRAH, BEEROTH, AND KIRIATH JEARIM WERE TAKEN, WITHOUT A DROP OF BLOOD BEING SPILT.

TO ENCOURAGE THE TRIBES TO CONTINUE WITH THE CONQUEST, JOSHUA DIVIDED THE DISTRICTS OF CANAAN AMONG THEM.

THE TRIBE OF LEVI, DEDICATED TO THE SERVICE OF GOD, WILL NOT HAVE ANY LAND, AS MOSES DECIDED.

REUBEN, GAD, AND THE HALF-TRIBE OF MANASSEH HAVE ALREADY RECEIVED THEIR PORTION FROM THE HAND OF MOSES HIMSELF.

MOSES PROMISED ME A REWARD. REMEMBER?

THAT'S RIGHT, CALEB, PRINCE OF JUDAH. I GIVE YOU HEBRON... TRY TO TAKE JERUSALEM.

GO THROUGH THE LAND. THEN COME AND TELL ME WHAT YOU'VE SEEN.

... THERE, IN THE NORTH, THE WATERS OF KINNERETH... AND FURTHER ON I SAW HAZOR, A FORTIFIED TOWN AMONGST THE HILLS...

GOOD! I'LL DRAW LOTS BEFORE THE LORD FOR THE OTHER SEVEN TRIBES.

ASHER
NAPHTALI
ZEBULUN
ISSACHAR
MANASSEH
JERICHO
Jordan
EPHRAIM
DAN
BENJAMIN
Jerusalem
GAD
JUDAH
Dead Sea
REUBEN
SIMEON
Beersheba

HOW THE PROMISED LAND WAS DIVIDED UP.

EACH TRIBE RECEIVED ITS TERRITORY ...

...AND SETTLED THERE, AT LAST!

THEN JOSHUA CHOSE SIX TOWNS OF REFUGE WHERE ANYONE WHO ACCIDENTALLY KILLED A MAN COULD TAKE REFUGE AND ESCAPE REVENGE.

48